IF YOU FIND A BABY BIRD

How To Protect and Care For Wild Baby Birds

TARA BOICE

Illustrated by Marjorie Sagar and Ernest C. Simmons

EDUCATIONAL ECOLOGY SERIES

SEAWIND PUBLISHING

NOTE

It is against State and Federal laws to permanently possess migratory wild birds as pets. Temporary possession is solely for the purpose of raising until such time as it can be successfully released into the wild.

PUBLISHED BY:

Seawind Publishing

18323 Sunset Boulevard, Redington Shores, Florida 33708

(813) 393-0933 / 391-2473

TEXT COPYRIGHT ● 1992 by Tara Boice

ILLUSTRATIONS COPYRIGHT ● 1992 by Marjorie Sager

BIRD IDENTIFICATION ILLUSTRATIONS COPYRIGHT

● 1992 by Ernest C. Simmons

DESIGN AND COVER ILLUSTRATION COPYRIGHT

● 1992 by Christina Evans

FIRST PRINTING 1992

ISBN: 0-9631916-0-8

LCCN: 92-080480

Printed in the United States of America

CONTENTS

FOREWORD

There are people who worry about species of birds and other animals and we call them conservationists. There are people who worry about individual birds and other animals and we call them humanitarians. And then there are people who care about both—the species and the individuals—and we call them Ralph Heath and the other people who work with him at the famous Suncoast Seabird Sanctuary.

This book can help you be like them. It will show you how you can help save both species and single creatures who will die if you are not there to join in the worldwide effort to save our fellow inhabitants of planet Earth.

Helping to save life, one creature at a time or by entire species, is very important work. It is far too important to do carelessly or without certain knowledge of how to do it right. This book has been long needed, for far too many people want to help, but do more harm than good.

The first problem is to know when animals really need your help and this book can guide you in solving that problem. It is sad indeed that too often people intrude into situations where the best thing they could have done is walk away and let nature be.

Intruding upon nature is a big decision, but it is sometimes necessary. This very badly needed book can help you decide not only when but how to do it. Read it carefully, then pitch in. One thing our fellow planeteers need is the good efforts of people of good will no matter what their age. Get your parents to help you, your grandparents, your brothers and sisters and your friends. All of you can chip in and be a part of the life-saving effort. Just be certain that every member of your team has read this book first.

1

WILD BABIES EVERYWHERE!

Birds are everywhere! There are 8,700 different species of birds. In almost every imaginable place on earth you'll find birds. They live everywhere that we do; in the arctic and in the tropics; from ocean to desert. It is their amazing ability to survive in a variety of climates that has made birds the most successful of the land vertebrates.

Birds are easy to find. Have you looked in your own backyard? They often build their nests very close to people and sometimes in unusual places. Don't be surprised if you find a nest in a hanging planter or even on your windowsill!

Since kids spend so much time outside, they find baby birds and other wild animals more often than anyone else. That is why it is especially important for them to respect and protect the animals that share our earth. There are species—such as the passenger pigeon once numbering in the millions—that have vanished because people hunted them into extinction. We need to protect wildlife so that other species of animals are not driven to extinction and lost to us forever.

There are many things that we can do to be a friend to wildlife. The first rule to remember is to "look but don't touch." Wild animals should never be handled unless necessary, and should always be observed from a distance.

Birds are easily frightened, so be careful not to get too close to them, especially during nesting season. Birds are good parents and they will energetically defend their offspring against potential predators. Have you ever had a bird swoop down at you from a tree or bush? This is how many birds protect their babies. Others will drag a wing along the ground pretending to

be injured. This "broken wing" technique tricks a predator into believing that the bird is easy prey; thus luring it away from the vulnerable chicks. So if you see a bird behaving strangely, chances are you are too close to its nest.

You should never take a baby bird out of its nest and take it home to raise. Adult birds are much better at taking care of their youngsters than people are. The chick's parents have learned how to care for their baby through a combination of instinct and imitation. They know exactly how to feed their chicks, and how frequently they should be fed. Baby birds are a lot of work! Did you know that a tiny sparrow is fed every fifteen minutes all day long?

But you may find a baby bird that is truly an orphan and needs your help. When this happens, you must realize that the bird must be released as soon as it is able to take care of itself. Wild birds have the right to be free. Many United States citizens feel the same way, so there are state and federal laws which make it illegal to keep wild birds permanently in captivity. It is your responsibility to release wild birds as soon as possible.

OUT OF THE NEST

It is hard to resist picking up and cuddling a tiny ball of feathers. There is nothing else that is quite as lovable as a baby bird. Just look! The poor thing is all by itself—it's been abandoned!

Stop! Before you pick up that tiny bundle, wait a moment. That helpless baby has probably jumped out of its nest for a reason. Many birds learn to fly from the ground up. So when baby birds grow into fledglings, they hop out of their nests and spend several days on the ground. They run back and forth and flap their wings. This exercises and strengthens their muscles so that they will be strong enough to fly. But they are not on their own yet! Their parents will continue to protect and feed them until they learn to forage for their own food.

So as you can see, many baby birds are right at home on the ground! Before you can decide whether or not the chick should be out of its nest, you must be able to tell how old it is. Birds go through two stages of growth before they become adults—nestling and fledgling. Nestlings are baby birds that have not yet left their nest. They have not grown all their feathers yet. Nestlings often appear naked, or they may have a soft downy fuzz instead of feathers. Their eyes may still be shut. If they have begun to grow feathers, there will be a bare spot underneath their wings. It's easy to catch a nestling. All you have to do is walk over and pick it up.

Nestlings are too young to run or fly away from you.

Fledglings are young birds that are ready to leave the nest. By this age they have grown lots of feathers. They are also very active—vigorously flapping their wings and hopping around. In fact, they often flap their wings so energetically that they raise themselves off the ground! This is how chicks learn to fly. Unlike nestlings, fledglings will run or fly away from you if you try to catch them.

Now you know the difference between a nestling and a fledgling. If the bird you found is a fledgling, the wisest thing to do is to shoo the bird into a protected area such as a shrub or clump of thick grass. Try to find a hiding place yourself. Then watch the chick for at least an hour—longer if possible to see if its parents come back to feed it.

6

Don't get too close, and be very quiet or the chick's parents will be afraid to return.

Since birds usually have more than one chick, it could take an hour or longer for its parents to return with a meal. This is because the other fledglings have probably scattered in all directions, and mom and dad have to find and feed each hungry mouth! The parents locate their babies by their constant cries for food, and they always know which babies are theirs.

The first thing to do for a nestling is to try to find its nest. If the nest is not in a nearby tree or bush, then try looking for it

on the ground. Many nests get knocked down by strong winds, thunderstorms, and cats. After you find the nest, put it in a secure spot such as in the fork of a tree. Then tie it in place with string or wire. Wrap the string or wire around the nest, and fasten it to a branch or the trunk of a tree.

If you can't find the original nest, you can make a new nest. A margarine container, a flower pot, or a hanging planter make great substitute nests. But make sure that there are holes in the bottom of any container that you use. The holes will allow the container to drain when it rains. This will keep it dry. Fill the new nest up to one inch below the rim with leaves, grass, or pine needles. If the babies are down too deep in the container, their parents will abandon them. Place the new nest close to the area where you found the bird, but keep it out of the direct sunlight.

Be careful when you pick the chick up. If it is well feathered, try to encourage it to step on a small stick or branch, then slowly lift it up to the nest. Babies that are too young to sit on a stick can be gently lifted by cupping your hands around its body. But don't squeeze too hard! Don't be afraid to pick the bird up. The belief that a parent bird will reject its chick if it is handled by a human is incorrect. That is because most birds have a poor sense of smell.

It is important to follow all of these steps before you decide the baby bird is an orphan and take it home to raise. The young bird needs its parents to teach it survival skills; for example, recognizing and escaping predators and foraging for food. The chick learns these skills through a process called imprinting. An infant bird will identify with whomever raises it. Birds raised by humans don't have the advantage of imprinting on members of their own species; this makes it difficult for them to learn the necessary skills needed for survival in the wild.

Now you can see why it is necessary to put a nestling back into its nest, or to wait and see if a fledgling's parents return to feed it. But there may be a time when you will find a chick that has been abandoned or somehow separated from its parents. If this has happened then the next chapter will tell you just what to do!

A NEW HOME

Baby birds are fragile creatures that need gentle handling. When you bring the youngster home everyone will want to touch it. Don't let them! Wild birds should not be handled any more than necessary. There are several good reasons for this. Touching the bird will disturb the delicate structure of its feathers. Have you ever seen a bird gently stroking each individual feather with its beak? This is called preening. Preening keeps the bird's feathers in good condition for flying. Frequent handling by people can permanently damage the bird's feathers; preventing it from flying until new feathers grow in to replace the damaged ones. Another important reason is that petting and playing with the chick will tame it--remember that it is a wild animal that you will soon be releasing back into its natural habitat. And always keep in mind that constant touching and handling is stressful for all young animals. Chicks are just like other babies—they need lots of rest.

Now that you have brought the chick home where should you put it? Birds need to be kept warm and dry, so the first thing to do is to make it a new home. The kind of home you will make will depend on whether the chick is a nestling or a fledgling.

A Home for a Nestling

Very young nestlings that are naked or have only a few feathers need to be kept warm all the time. The best home for them is a small box or bowl lined with tissue paper that is placed on a heating pad. (Do not line the container with hay or straw since these might contain bacteria that are harmful to baby birds.) Most heating pads have a low, medium, and high heat setting. Set the heat setting on low, then wrap a towel around the heating pad. Lay a thermometer on top of the towel to check the temperature. About 80 to 90 degrees Fahrenheit is just right. If it is over 90 degrees wrap a second towel around the heating pad. Place the heating pad with the towel wrapped around it in a cardboard box. Then place the container with the bird on top of the heating pad. With the top of the cardboard box open, lay a towel over the top. This will prevent drafts while still letting in air and light. You can also punch a few holes in the box to give the chick additional ventilation. Change the tissue paper in the small container several times a day.

Older nestlings that have grown a thin layer of feathers can be placed directly on the towel-wrapped heating pad. Layer the bottom of the box with newspaper, then lay the heating pad on the newspaper. Continue to place a towel over the top of the box and keep the heating pad on a low setting. Change the towel covering the heating pad at least once a day.

Another good place to keep young birds is in a plastic airline pet carrier. Line the carrier with a thick layer of newspaper, then place the heating pad on top of the newspaper. Wrap a towel

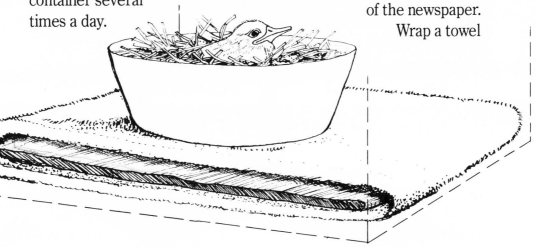

Heating pad wrapped in towel inside towel-draped box or airline pet carrier.

around the heating pad and place the chick on the towel. Drape a towel around the carrier to prevent drafts.

Nestlings should not be put in wire cages because they don't have enough feathers to stay warm in a cage. All birds— especially baby birds—should be kept away from drafts.

A Home For A Fledgling

By the time a chick grows into a fledgling it will have a thick layer of feathers over its entire body, and it will be much more active. Now it is time to make the chick a different kind of home.

Fledglings need to see their surroundings, so the best home for them is a cardboard box with windows cut in the sides. These windows can be six to eight inches square. Cut the windows out on two sides of the box. Then cut some fine mesh screen to fit over the square. Use two-inch wide duct tape to attach the screen to the box. This will allow more air and light into the box and allow the chick to see out. Now you can close the top of the box instead of covering it with a towel.

Fledglings like to sit on tree limbs and branches, so provide a perch for the chick. You can make a perch by poking a hole on two sides of the cardboard box and pushing a long stick through the holes. The stick must be very secure or it will roll, and the bird will be unable to perch on it. A stick with bark is better than a round perch bought in a pet shop, because a stick has an uneven surface that is easier for the bird to grip with its feet. Inspect the stick carefully for insecticide. Birds like to peck on wood and even a small amount of poison can be fatal. Place the perch in a comfortable position for the bird—not too close to the roof of the box.

Airline pet carriers are the best home for a fledgling. To make a perch in a carrier, push the stick through the grates on either side of the carrier. If there are no grates, you can place a stick on the floor, just make sure that it is wedged tightly between the sides of the carrier so that it will not roll.

Fledglings can be kept in a wire cage, but only if the bird is used to captivity. If you have raised the fledgling since it was a nestling, you can put it in a cage instead of a box or carrier. But if you have just found a wild fledgling, do not put it in a wire cage. A frightened bird will beat its wings against the wire bars and shred its feathers. The damaged feathers will make it impossible for the bird to fly until it grows a new set of feathers.

Now that the chick has grown feathers it will not need the warmth of a heating pad anymore. All you need to do is to line the bottom of the box, carrier, or cage, with a thick layer of old newspapers and change it daily. However, all birds are sensitive to drafts so don't put the fledgling near doors, windows, or air conditioning ducts.

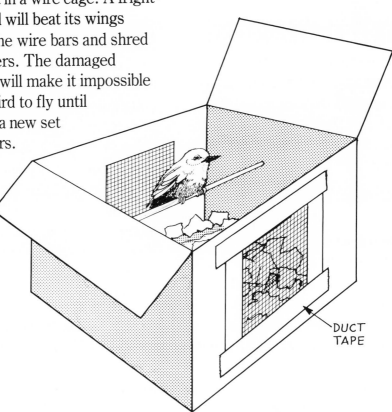

DUCT TAPE

FEEDING TIME

ould you eat in a restaurant that served egg yolk and dog food? You would if you were a baby bird! Baby birds require a special diet in order to stay healthy. Just as kids have to drink milk to grow big and strong, baby birds need their vitamins too. But don't give a baby bird milk! Birds cannot digest milk, and they get enough liquid in the special formula that you will learn how to prepare.

The formulas in this book are especially designed for song and garden birds. These are the small land birds that you find in your backyard. Other kinds of birds, such as seabirds and birds of prey called raptors, have a different kind of diet.

The bird's species determines whether it is a seed or meat eater, and whether it should be fed with an eyedropper or with tweezers. It is necessary for you to identify the bird correctly in order to feed it properly. You can turn to Chapter Nine for a description of some of the most common song and garden birds. If your bird's species is not in this chapter, you can check in your library or call your local chapter of the Audubon Society or bird club for help in identification. Your local SPCA will also have the address of the closest bird rehabilitation center.

The rehabilitation center can identify your bird for you, or care for it until it is old enough to be released into the wild.

Baby birds must be fed frequently. Very young nestlings should be fed every fifteen minutes. They eat as much or more than their own weight every day! Both nestlings and fledglings must be fed at least eight hours a day; up to fourteen hours a day if possible. The longer you can feed the bird, the better chance of survival it has.

The first formula is called the Emergency Formula. Because baby birds must eat so often, this easy formula was included to be used until you have a chance to prepare the regular formula. This formula does not have enough nutrients to keep the chick healthy, so it should not be used for longer then 24 hours. Baby birds eat only a tiny amount of food at one time, so put the extra formula in the

refrigerator until you need it. Then take out a small portion and let it warm up to room temperature before you feed the chick.

Make sure that you know what species you have before you attempt to feed it. Some species are primarily meat eating, while others eat seeds such as doves and pigeons. Doves and pigeons must be fed with an eyedropper, while other species can be fed with tweezers. Read the sections on feeding so you will know how to feed the chick correctly.

EMERGENCY FORMULA

MASHED HARD-BOILED EGG YOLK
WARM WATER
MIX IT TOGETHER UNTIL IT
IS MUSHY.

Which of the next two formulas you will use, will depend on the species of bird you have. The ingredients Nekton-S, and Nekton MSA can be purchased from a pet store or veterinarian.

The following formula is for doves and pigeons.

DOVE AND PIGEON FORMULA

2 1/4 OZ	JAR OF GERBER'S EGG YOLK
1/2 TBSP	GERBER'S HIGH PRO CEREAL (GOLDEN BOX)
1/8 TSP	NEKTON-S VITAMIN
1/8 TSP	NEKTON MSA
8 TSP	WARM WATER

How To Feed Nestling Doves And Pigeons

Doves and pigeons are a little more difficult to feed than other birds because they must be fed with an eyedropper. This has to be done carefully to prevent the bird from choking.

First you need an eyedropper that has a long, tapering point. This makes it easier to insert into the bird's crop. The crop of a dove is below the throat, at the base of the neck. The crop of a pigeon is on the right side of the throat. Not all birds have crops.

The crop is a pouch that is located in the gullet of certain birds where food is held and may even be partly digested. From here the food is gradually

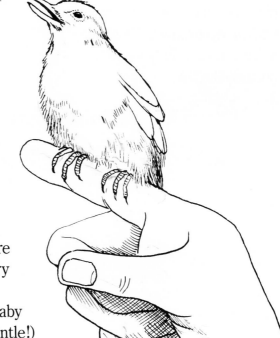

Then insert the eyedropper down the right side of the bird's throat, the bird's esophagus. The esophagus is the tube from the throat to the stomach through which food passes. *Don't confuse the esophagus with the trachea.* The middle tube is the bird's trachea or windpipe. If you squirt food into the trachea the bird will choke. When you are sure that the eyedropper is correctly inserted,

passed through the digestive tract of the bird.

Doves and pigeons do not open their mouths when they are hungry as do most other baby birds, so you must open their beaks by hand. First check the formula to be sure that it is lukewarm, then pry the beak open with your thumbnail. (The beaks of baby birds are very soft so be gentle!)

squeeze in the formula. Stop feeding when the chick's crop is full. You can tell that the crop is full when the bird's neck looks like a small balloon. It doesn't take much food to fill a tiny chick's crop.

Be especially careful not to overfeed doves. When a dove is overfed, its crop becomes plugged and it will be unable to digest its food. If the crop does not empty, wait for about an hour. The balloonlike crop should start to flatten out as the bird digests its food. If it does not, give the bird a small amount of yogurt.

Tiny, downy doves should be fed when the crop is empty. Feed older doves and pigeons every hour, or when the crop is empty. As the bird begins to grow more feathers you can gradually increase the time between feedings.

If the bird is not a dove or pigeon then use the following formula for other song and garden birds.

FORMULA FOR ALL OTHER SONG AND GARDEN BIRDS

1/2 CAN	HILL'S CANINE MAINTENANCE DOG FOOD
1/2 TSP	NEKTON-S VITAMIN
1 TSP	GERBER'S HIGH PRO CEREAL (GOLDEN BOX)
2 TBSP	WARM WATER

How To Feed All Other Nestling Song And Garden Birds

Only doves and pigeons need to be fed with an eyedropper. All other species of song and garden birds can be fed with tweezers. When the baby begs for food by opening its mouth wide and chirping, take the tweezers and break off a small amount of food. Place the food in the back of the bird's mouth. It should swallow on its own. If the bird does not open its mouth, then jiggle the box or gently tap on its beak. Once the nestling is full it will no longer beg.

Tiny sparrows and cedar wax-wings should be fed every ten minutes during the day. Mock-ingbirds, blue jays, cardinals, grackles, starlings, crows, robins and woodpeckers—every twenty minutes. As the bird gets bigger and grows feathers you can increase the time between feedings.

GROWING UP

As your nestling matures it needs adult food added to its diet. The kind of food it needs depends, of course, on the species of the bird. But all fledglings and adult birds need water. Give the chick water in a small dish. (A 1/2-inch deep mayonnaise jar lid is the perfect size.)

Also put out another jar lid with food in it. This will get the chick used to eating by itself. It takes between one and two weeks before the bird will eat entirely on its own, so you have to continue to hand feed your bird until it is completely independent.

How To Feed Fledgling Doves And Pigeons

When the chick begins to peck at the bottom of the box it is time to add seed to its diet. Sprinkle starter grain mash (you can get this at a pet store) on the floor of the cage or box. After a couple of weeks you can add a small amount of wild bird seed. You can be certain that the bird is feeding itself when you see that its crop is full of seeds.

How To Feed Fledgling Sparrows And Cardinals

As soon as the chick starts to peck at the floor of the box or at the meat formula on the tweezers, place a small jar lid of the formula sprinkled with parakeet seed in the box. Once the bird is eating on its own, gradually add wild bird seed to the bottom of the box and use less and less parakeet seed.

How To Feed All Other Fledgling Song And Garden Birds

Place a small jar lid of meat formula in the cage. For all other meat eating species listed in chapter nine except the woodpecker, you can also add a few pieces of cut fruit to the dish that contains the formula. You can feed the fledgling apples, grapes, or any other soft fruit that is cut into very tiny pieces.

Fledgling Care

What skill does the fledgling have yet to learn? How to fly, of course!

To give the bird a chance to learn how to fly, place it in an enclosed porch or bathroom. Just cover all the mirrors with newspaper or the fledgling will fly into them, and close the toilet lid. Remove anything that can break because birds are clumsy, especially when they are learning to fly.

Take the bird out of the box and place it gently on the floor. Once fledglings are out of the nest they learn to fly from the ground up. So don't ever teach a chick to fly by throwing it up in the air. It can be injured when it falls on the ground.

SAYING GOODBYE

Saying goodbye to an animal that you have raised is difficult. But there comes a time when you know that is exactly what you have to do. If you have done your job well, the fledgling will be a wild, healthy bird that will quickly become a part of its new environment. And who knows? The bird nesting outside your window next spring could be the orphan that you raised!

How do you know when a fledgling is ready to be released? The first clue is that the bird is feeding itself without help. The

next clue is that the chick will have grown all of its feathers. You should be able to look down on the bird's wings and tail and see that it is fully feathered without any bare patches. You should also see the fledgling flapping its wings back and forth very quickly. When it does this, the chick should be able to lift itself off the ground. Soon it will be able to fly!

So if the fledgling is fully feathered and feeding itself, it is ready to be released. But don't open the cage door yet! Just put the box or cage outside some-where safe out of the reach of cats and dogs. Leave the box or cage outside during the day, but bring it in at night. After a week open the cage door or remove the screen window of the box so that the bird can fly free. Now you can leave the open cage or box outside day and night for another week, while continuing to provide food and water. This gives the fledgling a chance to gradually become accustomed to its new environment. After a week the bird should be well ad-justed to its natural habitat, and you can congratulate yourself on a job well done!

BABIES IN YOUR BACKYARD

There are many other ways that you and your friends can help baby birds besides caring for an orphan. For instance, one thing that you can do is to check your yard and neighbor-hood for nesting birds. Nests can be made out of just about any-thing, and be almost anywhere.

So when you are outside, check carefully, there could be a nest even in the most unusual place.

For instance, robins build their nests in shrubs and trees, or even in the eaves of your house. They build sturdy nests. These nests are made of twigs, grass, and string and are lined with mud.

The nests that mourning doves build can be found almost anywhere. They build sloppy nests, using just a handful of twigs or straw. You can actually see the eggs through the sides or bottom of the nest, and for this reason they often fall out.

The blue jay also builds a rickety nest, but it is lined with grass, feathers, and leaves. Blue jays are attracted to bright objects and will often put pieces of shiny metal and bits of cloth in their nests. The blue jay builds its home in tall trees such as pines.

As you can see by these examples, birds' nests can be found in a variety of places and can be made of many different things. So look out for anything that might be a nest.

After you have spotted a nest, warn your parents about cutting down or pruning trees and shrubs that contain nests. This is especially important in the spring and early summer when the majority of bird species are nesting. If they accidentally cut down a tree with a bird's nest in it, they can cut out the section that contains the nest and attach it to a post. The post is then set into the ground near the location of the original nest.

The firemen of the Treasure Island Fire Department, in Treasure Island, Florida, found out how easy it is to relocate a nest safely. They found a nest of mourning doves in the large fire hose nozzle

on top of their ladder truck. They discovered this when they looked up, and saw a mourning dove flying in and out of the opening of the fire hose bringing food to her young.

Since the fireman could be called out at any time, the men knew that they had to relocate the nest. They knew that it had to be close to the original nest and hung up high for protection. Not having a plant hanger handy, they came up with an original and useful idea. They used a hubcap! They placed the nest carefully in the hubcap and hung it from the ceiling. The move didn't bother the mourning doves and for the firemen it was business as usual!

It is also a wise idea to warn your parents about spraying poison on their lawns and bushes. If birds eat these poisoned insects they will die. Poisoning birds will have the effect of allowing more insects to live and breed. That is because many species of birds feed on insects and this helps to control the insect population. It is double trouble in the springtime, because the parent birds will feed these insects to their chicks, thus poisoning both parent and offspring.

Another way to protect nesting birds is to build a fence about four or five feet high around the nesting site. A piece of old chicken wire will keep out most predators. All you have to do is get a piece of old wire fencing and circle the nest area with it. This works very well when the nesting site is in a low shrub or bush. If the nest is in a tree, place the fence two or three feet out from the base of the tree. This will keep a cat from climbing the tree and attacking the nest.

Try to keep dogs and cats away from nesting birds. You and your friends should keep an eye on Tabby and Rover during the spring when fledglings are learning to fly. Try to keep pets in the house or on a leash. If a cat must be let outside, put a collar with bells attached to it on the cat. This will help prevent the cat from sneaking up on a bird.

Sometimes when a bird picks a site to build its nest, it will pick a place near a window. When this happens the bird will see its reflection in the window and think another bird has taken its nesting place! The bird will attack its reflection in order to drive the intruder away. A bird can injure itself badly when it flies into the glass. But you can do something to help. You can tie a string across the window

horizontally, and attach strips of tin foil to the string. The string should be about 2/3 up the window from the windowsill. Cut the tin foil strips about two feet long and drape them across the string and then twist the strips together. This gives you two strips about a foot long each. Place the tin foil strips every two inches across the string.

Put out food and water for the hardworking parents. Just think, they have to feed their babies several times an hour for up to fourteen hours a day! You can buy wild bird seed at a pet shop or grocery store, or crush dry dog or cat food into small pieces for the meat eating birds to enjoy.

Make a bird bath! Birds love to take baths, especially in hot weather. You can make a bird bath by taking the lid of a garbage can and turning it upside down. Place it on a tree stump, table or any area that is off the ground and safe from predators. Then put the bath in a shady spot so the water stays cool.

Make observing and protecting a nestful of baby birds a fun school project. Ask your teacher if your class can make a group project out of observing and recording the progress of a nestful of baby birds. Then all of your friends can protect and learn about birds!

HELPFUL HINTS
Do's and Dont's for Raising Baby Birds

✓ Do handle the bird firmly but gently. Hold the wings folded close against the body when you pick it up.

✓ Do feed the bird at regular intervals through the day from dawn to dusk.

✓ Do have food and water available at all times for fledglings and older nestlings. Have you ever heard the expression "eat like a bird"? Unlike mammals, birds eat very tiny amounts of food all the time, so they must be able to drink and eat at any time during the day.

✓ Do remember the bird's natural diet. Candy and table scraps are NOT part of its diet.

✓ Do mix the formula in small amounts so it stays fresh.

✓ Do throw out unused formula and vitamins after six hours.

✓ Do keep the cage or box clean.

✓ Do keep the cage or box out of the direct sun and in an area away from drafts.

✓ Don't overheat a baby bird.

✓ Don't ever give a bird milk.

✓ Don't feed a baby bird water with a eyedropper. There is enough water in the formula for nestlings. Fledglings will drink out of a jar lid.

✓ Don't handle the infant unless necessary.

✓ Don't try to teach a fledgling to fly.

MEET THE BIRDS

Below are descriptions of some of the most common baby birds that you may find in your yard or neighborhood. Remember that identifying the species of the nestling or fledgling is important in feeding it the correct diet.

An important definition to know when identifying baby birds is the term gape flanges. Very young chicks often have a flabby fold of tissue around their beaks which look like lips. This tissue is called gape flanges, and will disappear as the chick matures.

BLUE JAY

Blue jays have blue or blue-gray feathers with white on the tips of their secondary (middle) wing feathers. They have dark bills and the inside of their mouth is bright red. Very young chicks have white gape flanges.

CARDINAL

The cardinal has red-brown feathers, and is usually bald around the eyes even when it is well feathered. It has a stout, heavy bill.

CEDAR WAXWING

It has a tan colored body. The black mask around the eye is rimmed with white. There is a crest on the back of the head, and the inside of its mouth is red.

CROW

The baby crow is completely black. The inside of its mouth is pink and it may have whiskers. It has has large, scaly feet.

GRACKLE

It is dark brown in color and has a bald area around the eye. There is a small hook on the end of its beak.

MOCKINGBIRD

The mockingbird has gray wings with big white patches on them. The inside of its mouth and gape flanges are yellow.

MOURNING DOVE

Young doves are covered with a yellowish fuzz, but when they are older they have dark brown feathers. They have very slender bills.

PIGEON

Pigeon chicks look very much like baby mourning doves. They are grey in color, except when except when they are very young, when they may have yellow fuzz on their head and neck. They have a large beak with bumps over their nostrils, and big thick feet.

ROBIN

The robin has a
dull orange breast
with dark spots, and
a white ring around
the eye. Its beak is
yellow, and the inside
of its mouth is orange.

SPARROW

Sparrows are very tiny. The
chick may be barely an inch
long. If it has feathers
they will be brown.
Its mouth is pink
edged with yellow.

STARLING

Young starlings
are dark brown in
color with light brown
edges on their upper wing
feathers. They have yellow
gape flanges.

WOODPECKER
(YELLOW-SHAFTED FLICKER)

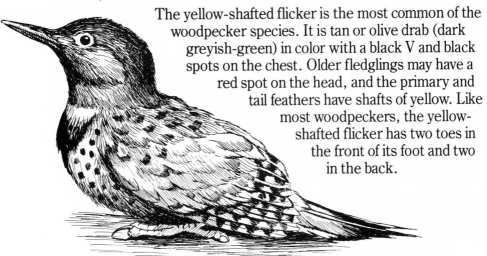

The yellow-shafted flicker is the most common of the woodpecker species. It is tan or olive drab (dark greyish-green) in color with a black V and black spots on the chest. Older fledglings may have a red spot on the head, and the primary and tail feathers have shafts of yellow. Like most woodpeckers, the yellow-shafted flicker has two toes in the front of its foot and two in the back.

GLOSSARY

CHICK — a young bird

CONSERVATIONIST — a person who is protecting something from loss, waste or harm.

EXTINCT — a species of plant or animal that no longer exists.

FORAGE — to look for food.

HABITAT — the surroundings in which an animal or plant lives and reproduces.

HUMANITARIAN — a person who spends time doing good for others.

PREDATOR — an animal that hunts and kills other animals for food.

SPECIES — a group of plants or animals which have similar characteristics in common and are able to breed among themselves.

VERTEBRATES — animals that have a backbone. Mammals, reptiles, fishes, and birds are all vertebrates.

INDEX

Illustrations appear on pages shown in italics.